Kaplan Publishing are constantly finding new ways to make a difference to your studies and our exciting online resources really do offer something different to students looking f[illegible] success.

This book comes with free MyKaplan [illegible]es so that you can study anytime, anywhere

Having purchased this book, you have access to the following online study materials:

CONTENT	ACCA (including FFA,FAB,FMA)		AAT		FIA (excluding FFA,FAB,FMA)	
	Text	Kit	Text	Kit	Text	Kit
iPaper version of the book	✓	✓	✓	✓	✓	✓
Interactive electronic version of the book	✓					
Progress tests with instant answers	✓		✓			
Mock assessments online			✓	✓		
Material updates	✓	✓	✓	✓	✓	✓
Latest official ACCA exam questions		✓				
Extra question assistance using the signpost icon*		✓				
Timed questions with an online tutor debrief using the clock icon*		✓				
Interim assessment including questions and answers	✓				✓	
Technical articles	✓	✓			✓	✓

* Excludes F1, F2, F3, FFA, FAB, FMA

How to access your online resources

Kaplan Financial students will already have a MyKaplan account and these extra resources will be available to you online. You do not need to register again, as this process was completed when you enrolled. If you are having problems accessing online materials, please ask your course administrator.

If you are already a registered MyKaplan user go to www.MyKaplan.co.uk and log in. Select the 'add a book' feature and enter the ISBN number of this book and the unique pass key at the bottom of this card. Then click 'finished' or 'add another book'. You may add as many books as you have purchased from this screen.

If you purchased through Kaplan Flexible Learning or via the Kaplan Publishing website you will automatically receive an e-mail invitation to MyKaplan. Please register your details using this email to gain access to your content. If you do not receive the e-mail or book content, please contact Kaplan Flexible Learning.

If you are a new MyKaplan user register at www.MyKaplan.co.uk and click on the link contained in the email we sent you to activate your account. Then select the 'add a book' feature, enter the ISBN number of this book and the unique pass key at the bottom of this card. Then click 'finished' or 'add another book'.

Your Code and Information

This code can only be used once for the registration of one book online. This registration and your online content will expire when the final sittings for the examinations covered by this book have taken place. Please allow one hour from the time you submit your book details for us to process your request.

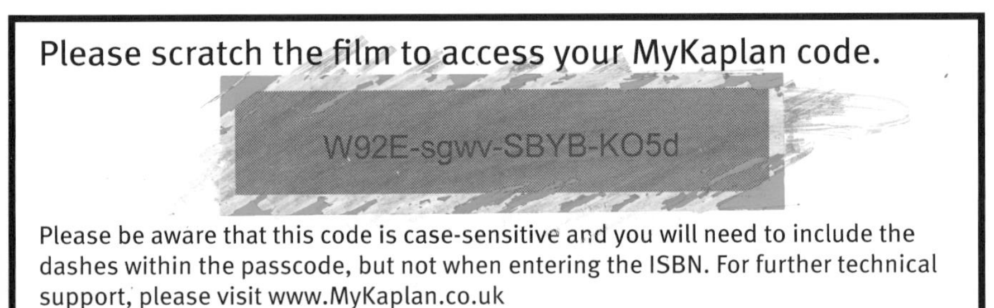

Professional Examinations

AQ2013 Level 3

Spreadsheet Software

REVISION KIT

British Library Cataloguing-in-Publication Data

A catalogue record for this book is available from the British Library.

Published by:

Kaplan Publishing UK

Unit 2 The Business Centre

Molly Millar's Lane

Wokingham

Berkshire

RG41 2QZ

ISBN: 978-0-85732-899-1

Printed and bound in Great Britain.

CONTENTS

The answers to the tasks in these scenarios can be found as spreadsheet files on your MyKaplan account (together with one text file for Scenario 1).

Please go to www.mykaplan.co.uk and login using your username and password.

You will find a wealth of other resources to help you with your studies on the AAT website:

www.aat.org.uk/

Section 1

SCENARIO TASKS

SCENARIO 1

SLICK PARTZ

Time Allowed 90 Minutes

You are an Accounting Technician working for the UK Branch of a company called **Slick Partz**. Your branch is a Franchise of the parent company which is based in Europe. Slick Partz manufactures parts for hospital equipment at its factory in Poland and these are then sold to franchisees. The franchise is then responsible for selling the parts to hospitals in its sales area.

The franchise buys the parts from the parent company in Euros (€) but sells to the hospitals in GB Pounds (£).

You have been sent a file in text format by your Managing Director and he wants you to carry out some work on it using a spreadsheet package. The text file can be found on MyKaplan. If you are doing this scenario in centre you will be told where to find the file.

If you are doing this exercise at your training provider you should save your work after each task to the folder designated for that purpose. If you are doing the exercise on your own computer we recommend that you create a folder to save your work in.

Required:

TASK 1

The MD would like you to convert the 'Text File' to a worksheet.

(a) Open a blank workbook.

(b) Import the 'Slick Partz' text file into Sheet 1/ cell A1.

(c) In Column D format the 'Cost_Price' as currency. It should be formatted as Euros to 2 decimal places.

(d) In Column E format the 'Sales_Price' as currency. It should be formatted to GB Pounds to 2 decimal places.

(e) Save the workbook as Slick Partz in the 'Exam Kit Solutions' folder.

(f) Rename Sheet 1 as 'Data Import'

(g) Copy the 'Data Import' worksheet in the same workbook and rename it as Subtotals

(h) Save the workbook as 'Scenario 1 – Slick Partz'

TASK 2

You are required to sort the data in the 'Subtotals' worksheet in preparation for carrying out subtotalling. The subtotals that are needed are for Model and Tele_Sales_Operative.

(a) Create subtotals for Model, summing the Sales quantity.

(b) Create a further subtotal for Tele_Sales_Operative, summing the Sales quantity.

(c) Convert the worksheet to show formulas.

(d) Save the workbook.

TASK 3

Create a new workbook called 'Currency Conversion'.

(a) Return to the 'Data Import' worksheet.

(b) Auto-Filter the data in the worksheet.

(c) Filter by 'Monty Video'.

(d) Copy the result and paste it into Cell A1 in a blank worksheet in the Slick Partz workbook.

(e) Rename the worksheet as 'Currency Conversion'.

(f) Return to the 'Data Import' worksheet and remove the 'Monty Video' filter.

(g) Save the workbook.

TASK 4

Convert the cost prices to GB Pounds (£).

(a) Open the 'Currency Conversion' worksheet.

(b) Insert 3 rows at the top of the worksheet.

(c) Insert a new column into Column 'E'.

(d) In Cell D1, type Conversion Rate.

(e) Make the font bold and underline the text. Format D1 to Right Justified.

(f) Format Cell E1 to number to 2 decimal places and type 0.84.

(g) In Cell E4 type Cost_Price_GBP(£).

(h) Make the font bold in cells A4:I4.

(i) Autofit column widths.

(j) In Cell E5:E26 create a formula that converts the content of Cell D5:D26 to GBP(£). Use the conversion rate in Cell E1. Give regard to the potential need to change the conversion rate.

(k) Format Cells E5:E26 to GBP(£), to 2 decimal places.

(l) Copy the currency conversion worksheet within the Slick Partz workbook and rename the new worksheet as Profit Calculation.

(m) Return to the currency conversion worksheet and show formulas. Autofit column widths.

(n) Save the workbook.

TASK 5

Calculate the profit from the converted figures and supply some statistics.

(a) Open the 'Profit Calculation' worksheet and auto-fit column widths if necessary.

(b) In Cells J4, K4 and L4 create 3 new headings of 'Total Cost', 'Total Revenue' and 'Profit'. Use the same format as on earlier headings.

(c) In Cell J5:J26 create a formula that multiplies Cost_Price_GBP(£) by Sales Quantity.

(d) In Cell K5:K26 create a formula that multiplies Sales Price by Sales Quantity.

(e) In Cell L5:L26 create a formula that calculates Profit (Total Revenue – Total Cost).

(f) In Cell J29 create a formula that calculates the average Cost, do the same for Total Revenue and Profit in adjacent cells. Create a suitable heading in I29.

(g) In Cell J30:L30 create formulas that calculate the largest number in each of the data sets. Create a suitable heading in I30.

(h) In Cell J31:L31 create formulas that calculate the smallest number in each of the data sets. Create a suitable heading in I31.

(i) Show formulas and auto-fit column widths.

(j) Save the workbook.

TASK 6

Create a pivot table to show how many units each tele-sales operative has sold, and produce a pivot chart to show your results.

(a) Open the Data Import worksheet.

(b) Clear auto-filter.

(c) Using the data in Cells A1:H97 create a simple Pivot Table that shows 'Sales Quantity' by Tele_Sales_Operative, within Model. Model should be used as the Column Field.

(d) Rename the worksheet 'Pivot'.

(e) Remove Grand Totals for Rows and Columns.

(f) Create a Pivot Chart and locate it on the Pivot worksheet. The type of chart should be a Clustered Column Chart.

(g) Copy and paste the chart in the same location and convert the new chart to a 3D Pie Chart. Change the chart location to a chart sheet. Rename this as Chart Sheet. Add a suitable title and show percentages as data labels.

(h) Add Customer as a Page Field.

(i) Save the workbook.

TASK 7

The MD wants you to create a spreadsheet that is able to look up the cost price of a particular product and return the stock quantity.

(a) Create a new Worksheet and rename it 'Product Lookup'.

(b) Merge Cells B2: D3. Place a border around the merged cells, make the fill grey and format the cell bold, font sized 12.

(c) Go to Cell B6. Place a border around the Cell, make the fill grey and format the cell bold, font sized 12 and currency € Euro (€123) to 2 decimal places.

(d) Go to Cell B9. Place a border around the cell, make the fill grey and format the cell bold, font sized 1.

(e) Go to Cell B12. Place a border around the cell, make the fill grey and format the cell bold, font sized 12.

(f) Create a VLOOKUP that looks up a Product-Code on the Data Import worksheet and places its Cost_Price in Cell B6. The Product-Code should be found when it is typed into Cell B2. The VLOOKUP should be set to look for only exact matches. If Cell B2 is empty the VLOOKUP should not return an error message.

(g) Create a VLOOKUP that looks up a Product-Code on the Data Import worksheet and places its Stock_Quantity in Cell B9. The Product-Code should be found when it is typed into Cell B2. The VLOOKUP should be set to look for only exact matches. If Cell B2 is empty the VLOOKUP should not return an error message.

(h) In Cell B12, create a formula that produces the word "Re-order" if the value in Cell B9 is greater than 0 but less than 20.

(i) Set Conditional Formatting to Cell B2 so that the cell has a red border, bright yellow fill and a pattern when something is entered into the cell.

(j) Set Conditional Formatting to Cell B6 so that the cell has a black fill and white text when something is entered into the Cell B2.

(k) Set Conditional Formatting to Cell B9 so that the cell has a black fill and white text when something is entered into the Cell B2.

(l) Set Conditional Formatting to Cell B12 so that the cell has a black fill and white text when the value of F6 is greater than 0 but less than 20.

(m) Show formulas and Autofit column widths.

(n) Set page orientation to 'Landscape'.

(o) Save the workbook.

SCENARIO 2

BETTABAKE

Time Allowed 90 Minutes

You work for a small bakery. They are very good at making cakes but not very good at doing their budgets. They are constantly running out of material because they don't predict accurately what cakes they are going to make that day.

The company makes four different cakes.

The Whirl

Splash

Butterbun

Chocco

Ingredient requirements for each product are:

	Eggs	*Flour*	*Sugar*	*Butter*	*Cream*
The Whirl	1	50g	35g	28g	12g
Splash	1.5	30g	18g	22g	10g
Butterbun	2	65g	27g	24g	0
Chocco	1	55g	30g	21g	0

The following information is also available with regards to selling prices. It costs:

£1.50	for	12 eggs
£1.80	for	200g of flour
£2.20	for	200g of sugar
£6.00	for	1kg of butter
£2.50	for	300g of cream.

If you are doing this exercise at your training provider you should save your work after each task to the folder designated for that purpose. If you are doing the exercise on your own computer we recommend that you create a folder to save your work in.

Required:

The Production Manager wants you to prepare a spreadsheet that will help her with her budgets.

1 **Set up a new spreadsheet for the scenario. Save this file as 'Scenario 2 – Bettabake'. The spreadsheet will need 4 worksheets.**

Rename:

Worksheet 1	Ingredients
Worksheet 2	Cost per unit
Worksheet 3	Cost per cake
Worksheet 4	Budget

2 **On the 'Ingredients' worksheet:**

(a) Input the ingredient requirements for each cake.

(b) Start the table at Cell A4.

(c) Row and column headers should be in bold.

(d) Save your work.

3 **On the 'Cost per unit' worksheet: starting in Cell A1**

- Calculate:

  (i) the cost per egg.

  (ii) the cost per gram of butter.

  (iii) the cost per gram of sugar.

  (iv) the cost per gram of flour.

  (v) the cost per gram of cream.

- Four columns will be required:

  (i) Ingredients

  (ii) Total Cost – format as currency £ to 2 decimal places.

  (iii) No of Units – format as number to 0 decimal places.

  (iv) Cost per Unit – format as numbers to three decimal places.

4 **On the 'Cost per cake' worksheet: starting at Cell A1**

- Calculate the cost for each cake, using the 'Ingredients' worksheet and the 'Cost per unit' worksheet.
- The cost for each ingredient per cake will be needed.
- A column for 'Total Cost per Cake' will be required.
- A column will be required for the products and the ingredients.
- Use relative and absolute cell referencing when doing the formulas.
- Format your cells as numbers to 3 decimal places.
- Show formulas and auto-fit column widths.
- Save your work

5 **On the 'Budget' worksheet:**

- Create a formula so that the Production Director can type in any quantity of each cake and the spreadsheet will calculate for her, how much of each ingredient is required.
- Starting in Cell A3 you will need to create a row header for each cake. Along the side of each cake you will need a cell for each quantity of cake.
- Starting in Cell D2 you will need a column heading for each type of ingredient
- In the cells beneath these headings create a formula that calculates the quantity of ingredients required to manufacture the volume of cakes entered in Column B.
- Beneath your table of data you will require totals for each ingredient.

- Beneath your totals for each ingredient you need to create a formula to calculate purchase quantity for each ingredient. Eggs are purchased in boxes of 360 all other ingredients are purchased by the kg (1000g).
- Beneath the purchase quantity create an expression that rounds the purchase quantity up to the nearest whole box or kg
- Manufactured quantities should be: The Whirl 850; Splash 9; Butterbun 15; Chocco 24.

6 **The current selling prices for each cake are:**

	£
The Whirl	0.90
Splash	1.20
Butterbun	1.10
Chocco	1.50

- Starting at Row 15 on the budget spreadsheet, calculate whether the individual products are making a profit or a loss.
  - It will be necessary to see the product name; its cost price, its selling price and the calculation for profit.
  - Look up the cost price from the 'Cost per Cake' worksheet.
- Use conditional formatting (turn the cell red) where a product is loss making.
- Show formulas and auto-fit to columns.
- Save your work.

SCENARIO 3

CRAZY CARS

Time Allowed 90 Minutes

You work as a payroll assistant for a car sales company called Crazy Cars.

The sales staff are paid a basic wage plus commission for the cars that they sell.

There are 7 sales people, whose start dates at the company are as follows.

Name:	**Start Date:**
Ryan Lee	14/01/2009
Simon Mozley	28/03/2007
Jack Brown	08/02/2004
Stuart Gregson	01/09/2002
Linda Green	14/11/2003
Bev Jones	31/10/2007
Baldeep Lad	16/08/2005

Basic wage

The basic wage is dependent on the number of full years each employee has worked for the business.

An employee's starting rate (for the first 12 months) is £160 per week.

The basic rate per week increases by 10% for each full year of employment up to a maximum of 5 years.

A year = 365 days.

Commission earned

Each employee receives 5% of the profit they have earned from each car they have sold that week.

If a car is sold at a loss, then 5% of this loss is deducted from the employee's commission.

Any cars sold at a loss must be highlighted for the Finance Manager.

Weekly bonus

The member of staff who earns the most commission each week receives an extra £100 bonus.

If you are doing this exercise at your training provider you should save your work after each task to the folder designated for that purpose. If you are doing the exercise on your own computer we recommend that you create a folder to save your work in.

Car Sales this week

Car Type	*Cost*	*Sales Value*	*Sold by:*
Alfa Romeo (Brera Coupe)	£8,500	£14,000	Stuart Gregson
Audi A3 (Hatchback)	£9,400	£11,299	Simon Mozley
BMW 1 Series	£7,800	£12,600	Ryan Lee
Cadillac BLS Saloon	£11,000	£13,950	Bev Jones
Chevrolet Aveo	£3,400	£4,590	Linda Green
Chevrolet Captiva Estate	£10,900	£12,400	Jack Brown
Chevrlet Matiz	£1,800	£3,400	Bev Jones
Chrysler Voyager	£8,100	£9,300	Simon Mozley
Citroen Berlingo	£11,400	£10,300	Baldeep Lad
Dodge Journey	£11,200	£13,300	Stuart Gregson
Fiat 500 Hatchback	£4,400	£8,300	Baldeep Lad
Fiat Punto	£3,900	£4,400	Ryan Lee
Ford Fiesta	£8,200	£8,400	Ryan Lee
Ford Focus	£8,600	£9,000	Baldeep Lad
Ford Fusion	£6,800	£6,600	Bev Jones
Hyundai 130	£8,200	£9,000	Linda Green
Jeep Patriot	£7,800	£9,100	Baldeep Lad
Kia Carens	£6,200	£7,000	Ryan Lee
Kia Ceed	£7,400	£10,000	Jack Brown
Kia Picento	£5,900	£6,600	Jack Brown
Lexus Saloon	£11,800	£15,400	Linda Green
Mini Cooper (Hatchback)	£8,800	£9,400	Stuart Gregson
Nissan Almera	£7,900	£8,400	Bev Jones
Nissan Micra	£5,100	£6,400	Linda Green
Peugeot 107	£3,800	£6,100	Simon Mozley

Required:

1 **Set up a new spreadsheet for the scenario. Save this file as 'Scenario 3 – Crazy Cars'. The spreadsheet will need 4 worksheets.**

Rename:

Worksheet 1	Employee Information
Worksheet 2	Basic Pay
Worksheet 3	Car Sales Information
Worksheet 4	Total Pay

Save your work.

2 **On the 'Employee Information' worksheet:**

(a) Starting at Cell A1, using suitable headings, input the employee names and their employment start dates.

(b) In the next column and using the TODAY function – calculate the number of days each employee has worked for Crazy Cars. Place the TODAY function in Cell B10. Add a suitable heading in Cell A10. Place the number of days in a year in Cell B12 with a suitable heading in A12. Use absolute and relative referencing where appropriate.

(c) In the next column (D) convert the number of days into years (Use the ROUNDDOWN function in Column (E) to round down the years).

(d) Show formulas and auto-fit column widths.

(e) Save your work.

3 **On the 'Basic Pay' worksheet:**

(a) Using the information from the scenario, calculate the weekly pay for an employee at the company based on 0 to 10 full years of employment.

(b) Start your table in Cell A1, using suitable headings for both columns.

(c) Add a border around each cell.

(d) Show formulas and auto-fit column widths.

(e) Save your work.

4 **On the 'Car Sales Information' worksheet:**

(a) Starting in Cell A1 and using suitable headings for each vehicle sold, input: the model; the sales person; sales value; and cost.

(b) In the next column create an expression to determine the profit made for each vehicle.

(c) In the next column calculate the amount of commission earned on each vehicle.

(d) All monetary values should be formatted to currency (£) to 2 decimal places.

(e) Use conditional formatting to identify any vehicles that have been sold at a loss. Have the cell turn red with black text.

(f) Show formulas and auto-fit column widths.

(g) Save your work.

5 **Create a simple pivot table to show the commission each employee has earned.**

(a) The employees name should be used as the row column.

(b) Save the Pivot Table worksheet as 'Pivot'.

6 **On the 'Total Pay' worksheet:**

(a) Type the following headings into the cells given:

(i)	Employee	A1
(ii)	Number of Years	B1
(iii)	Guaranteed Pay	C1
(iv)	Commission	D1
(v)	Bonus	E1
(vi)	Total pay for the week	F1

(b) Show the following information:

(i) Column A, using Data Validation create a drop down list for all employees (the list of employees will need to be entered on this worksheet – use column K).

(ii) Column B, use a VLOOKUP from the 'Employee Information' tab to extract the number of years each employee has been employed.

(iii) Column C, Use a VLOOKUP from the Basic Pay worksheet, to calculate the applicable basic weekly pay for each employee.

(iv) Column D, Use a VLOOKUP from the Pivot table worksheet, enter the Commission earned per employee.

(v) Column E, determine which employee has earned the most commission and therefore will earn the weekly bonus of £100, hard key the figure against the correct employee.

(vi) Column F, Using the Sum function – calculate the total pay for each employee for the week and the total wages the company are paying that week.

(vii) Show formulas and auto-fit column widths.

7 **Create a Pie Chart for the Finance Director to show each sales person's contribution to the total commission earned.**

(a) Check that the person you have allocated the weekly bonus to has the largest share of the pie!

(b) Save this on a new worksheet called 'Pie Chart'. Label the chart appropriately.

(c) Percentages must be shown on the Pie Chart.

8 **Format the worksheets so that each worksheet is on one page.**

SCENARIO 4

GOODTIME TRAVEL

Time Allowed 90 Minutes

Goodtime Travel is a firm of Travel Agents that specialises in long haul package holidays. They buy the flights and hotel rooms in bulk from the airlines and hotels. They are a reputable firm and get most of their custom from customers who have used their service before.

They have recently invested in a marketing campaign to try and encourage new customers to use their service. The Marketing Manager has said that the campaign will be viewed as a success if at least 25% of income each week is generated from new customers.

Goodtime Travel only flies from Heathrow.

Repeat customers

Customers can receive discounts off their holidays. A discount will only be given if a customer has booked their previous bookings with Goodtime Travel. A discount is given of 1p per mile flown on the previous holiday.

This discount is then deducted from the price of the current holiday. However, the Finance Director is considering adapting the discount rates so that they are different for each destination.

Miles (round trip) from Heathrow

Destination	*Miles*
Sydney	21200
Fiji	20218
Cape Town	12010
Los Angeles	17500
Hong Kong	12104
Rio De Janeiro	18004
Kuala Lumpar	13104
Auckland	22774
Beijing	10140
Tokyo	11874
Colombo (Sri Lanka)	10816

The following bookings have been made this week

Customer No	*Destination*	*Holiday price*	*Repeat*	*Previous Destination*
1	Cape Town	£3,200	Yes	Sydney
2	Rio De Janeiro	£2,400	No	Not applicable
3	Tokyo	£1,250	No	Not applicable
4	Kuala Lumpar	£1,295	Yes	Fiji
5	Sydney	£3,800	No	Not applicable
6	Los Angeles	£2,400	No	Not applicable
7	Los Angeles	£1,800	Yes	Los Angeles
8	Colombo (Sri Lanka)	£2,250	No	Not applicable
9	Rio De Janeiro	£1,950	Yes	Colombo (Sri Lanka)
10	Cape Town	£1,880	No	Not applicable
11	Auckland	£2,200	Yes	Sydney
12	Los Angeles	£2,250	No	Not applicable
13	Auckland	£2,150	No	Not applicable
14	Sydney	£1,950	Yes	Beijing
15	Los Angeles	£2,400	No	Not applicable
16	Hong Kong	£1,850	No	Not applicable
17	Tokyo	£1,600	Yes	Rio De Janeiro
18	Rio De Janeiro	£1,950	Yes	Los Angeles
19	Colombo (Sri Lanka)	£1,750	No	Not applicable
20	Kuala Lumpar	£1,400	Yes	Tokyo
21	Rio De Janeiro	£1,650	No	Not applicable
22	Sydney	£2,250	No	Not applicable

Required:

1 **Set up a new spreadsheet for the scenario. Save this file as 'Scenario 4 – Goodtime Travel'. The spreadsheet will need 3 worksheets.**

Rename:

Worksheet 1 Discounts

Worksheet 2 Weekly sales

Worksheet 3 What IF Analysis

2 **On the 'Discounts' worksheet:**

(a) Starting at Cell A3, Input the all possible destinations, and their associated air-miles. Create suitable headings.

(b) You will need to add 'Not applicable' to the list of destinations, for customers who have not booked through Goodtime Travel before, with associated air-miles of 0.

(c) In Cell E1 enter the discount rate given in the scenario and give it a suitable heading in D1.

(d) In Column C create a formula to calculate the discount for a particular destination. The Marketing Manager is considering changing the discount per mile, therefore use appropriate absolute and relative referencing.

(e) Format the discount column as currency (£) to 2 decimal places.

(f) Show formulas, auto-fit column widths and save your work.

3 **On the 'Weekly Sales' worksheet:**

(a) Enter this week's sales information, from the information given in the task data.

(b) Create a Discount column. Use a VLOOKUP from the 'Discounts' worksheet to calculate any applicable discounts.

(c) Format currency to 2 decimal places in £.

(d) In another column, use Auto-sum to calculate the amount owing for each booking deducting any discounts for repeat customers.

4 **Create a pivot table in a new worksheet and call this worksheet 'Pivot':**

(a) Show how much revenue has been generated from new customers compared to existing customers. Use 'Repeat' as the row field.

(b) On the Pivot sheet create an expression to calculate the % of income generated from new customers. This should be located underneath the pivot table.

(c) Use an IF function – based on the outcome of task 4b – for the Marketing Director to determine whether the campaign was a success.

(i) If more than 25% of income is generated from new customers = Successful campaign.

(ii) If less than 25% of income is generated from new customers = Unsuccessful campaign.

(iii) Format the outcome of the IF formula by making it bold, and enlarging the text to font size 16.

(d) Show formulas, auto-fit column width and save your work.

5 **The Finance Director is considering changing the discount on offer per mile for repeat customers. He wants the discounts for the following destinations changed to:**

Destination	**New Discount**	**Currently**	**Comments**
Sydney	£130.00	£212.00	Decrease discount as currently too high
Fiji	£275.00	£202.18	Increase discount to instigate more sales.

On the What IF Analysis worksheet:

(a) Copy the Discount information from the discount worksheet into the What IF Analysis worksheet.

(b) Using What IF Analysis – **Goal Seek**, calculate a revised discount rate per mile for both Sydney and Fiji to achieve the discounts the Finance Director has asked for.

(i) Calculate the discount rate per mile for Sydney. Copy and **'paste–special values'** the result to Row 15. Provide a suitable heading for the solution. Format the result cell as bright yellow.

(ii) Calculate the discount rate per mile for Fiji. Copy and **'paste–special values'** the result to Row 24. Provide a suitable heading for the solution. Format the result cell as bright yellow.

(iii) Reset the original discount rate per mile to 1p.

(c) Show formulas, auto-fit column width and save your work.

SCENARIO 5

STAR TICKETS

Time Allowed 90 Minutes

You work for Star Tickets, a small company selling tickets to music concerts.

They sell their tickets over the phone and record their sales in a notebook stored in the office. They only have one notebook which means that only one person can write in the notebook at any one time.

The company has weekly targets that they should meet with regards to ticket sales but it is currently proving very difficult to measure staff performance using the current system. Customers also pay in instalments for the tickets and it is proving difficult to keep track of how much each customer has left outstanding for their tickets.

Management have said that at the end of each day the total outstanding balance owed by customers cannot be greater than 5% of the total sales generated that day. Management are also aware that some of the tickets are for artists who are not popular and are therefore, not making profit for the company but they are unsure as to which artists these might be.

Star Tickets have contacted you to help them create a spreadsheet to help manage their ticket sales. They have given you the notebook to look at for today's sales:

Artist and Customer Payment	**Ticket Seller**
Cliff Richard (Paid: £10 towards the £30 bill for Saturday showing)	Jane
Take That (Paid in full £60 for Tuesday performance)	Mark
The Drifters (Paid in full £90 for Wednesday performance)	Mark
Beyoncé (Paid £80 for Friday)	Karen
Take That (Paid half of £30 for Tuesday showing)	Jane
Cliff Richard (Paid in full £45 for Saturday showing)	Mark
The Drifters (Paid £34 for Friday's performance)	Jane

Star Tickets buy their weekend tickets directly from the concert venues for £50 per ticket (These include Friday tickets). If tickets are sold for more than the purchase price, half of the profit on the ticket is paid out to the Ticket seller as a bonus and the other half is retained by Star Tickets as profit.

Star Tickets are offered the following discounts by the concert venues for their weekday tickets

Monday – Wednesday 25%

Thursday – 10%

Staff can sell the tickets for whatever price they like. The higher the selling price, the larger the bonus they will earn.

Required:

Star Tickets

Scenario Objectives:

- To show how much is outstanding to pay on each ticket.
- The price paid by Star Tickets to the concert venue for each of their tickets.
- The profit made for each ticket.
- To show whether or not each ticket seller receives a bonus for each sale.
- Whether the amount outstanding from customers to pay is at an acceptable level.
- A note to management of which artists (if any) are not bringing profit to the company.
- A note to management of which ticket sellers are not bringing profit to the company (and any possible reasons for this).

1 **Create a new workbook, call this 'Scenario 5 – Star Tickets'.**

2 **Rename the first worksheet – 'Ticket Sales'; Rename the second worksheet – 'Data'.**

3 **Starting in Cell A1 the Ticket Sales worksheet needs the following headings:**

Artist

Days of week

Purchase price

Sales price

Amount paid

Amount outstanding

Profit/loss

Ticket seller

Bonus payable?

Notes:

- Star Tickets only sell tickets for Take That, Beyoncé, The Drifters and Cliff Richard.
- Karen, Mark and Jane are the only employees.

(a) On the 'Data' worksheet – create named ranges for Artist; Day of Week; and Ticket Seller.

(b) On the 'Data' worksheet, create a table of information showing: the discounted prices that Star Tickets would pay from the venues on the different days of the week; the original price; and the discount percentage. Provide suitable headings.

(c) On the Ticket Sales worksheet use 'Data Validation' to create drop down lists for Artist; Day of Week; Ticket Seller.

(d) In the Purchase Price column on the Ticket Sales worksheet, create a VLOOKUP that selects the correct purchase price based on the day of the week.

(e) In the Amount Outstanding column create a formula that takes the Amount Paid from the Sales Price.

(f) In the Profit/Loss column create a formula that takes the selling price from the purchase price.

(g) In the Bonus Payable? Column, create an IF function to determine whether a bonus is payable. If a bonus is payable the function should return Yes if not then the function should return No.

4 **Enter the data from the scenario into the 'Ticket Sales' worksheet.**

(a) Make sure that all formulas are copied down correctly.

(b) Use conditional formatting to turn cells red where a loss has been made.

(c) Create totals below the 'Sales Price' and the 'Amount Outstanding' column. Create the totals in Row 11. Use single line border at the top of these cells and double line border at the bottom of the cells.

(d) Any cells on the Ticket Sales worksheet which require manual input need to be highlighted green.

(e) Any cells which are updated via formulas (automatically) need to be highlighted yellow.

(f) In Row 20 on the Ticket Sales worksheet , create a formula that determines the percentage of the total Amount Outstanding in comparison to the total of Sales Price. Provide a suitable heading.

(g) In the same row create an IF Function that determines whether the percentage in 4(f) would be acceptable to management. i.e. Not more than 5% of total sales value. The function should return either OK or Not Acceptable.

5 **Show formulas, auto-fit column width and save your work.**

6 **Create a pivot table to show how much profit each ticket seller has made, by Artist.**

(a) Create a new worksheet for this and call it 'Pivot'.

7 **In a brief note to management explain:**

(a) Which artists (if any) are not bringing profit to the company.

(b) Which ticket sellers are not bringing profit to the company (and any possible reasons for this).

(c) Write the answers on the Pivot Worksheet.